# I love my Granny and Grandpa too!

**Written and Illustrated**
**by the Grandchildren of Great Britain**

**Introduced by**
**Jimmy & Irene Greaves**

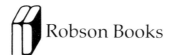
Robson Books

Front cover picture by Max Keble-White
Back cover picture by Rebecca
Pictures on pages 1, 2 and 3 by Matthew King, aged 6,
Leanne Williams, aged 7, and Amy Jones, aged 6

Edited by Sam Westmacott

I and me to love my grancha he and spoils takes me School

First published in Great Britain in 1989 by Robson Books Ltd,
Bolsover House, 5-6 Clipstone Street, London W1P 7EB.

Copyright © 1989 TV-am

Compiled for TV-am by Complete Editions Ltd

**British Library Cataloguing in Publication Data**

I love my granny – and grandpa too!
  1. Grandparents
  I. TV-am
  306.817
ISBN 0-86051-630-X

Typeset by Ian Greig Ltd
Printed and bound in Great Britain by
Butler & Tanner Ltd, Frome and London

# Introduction

One of the great joys of getting older (let's face it, one of the few joys of getting older) is becoming a grandparent. Because we had our four children while we were young we've had the pleasure of greeting the arrival of seven grandchildren while we've been comparatively young too. Seven so far, that is, but still counting.

There is nothing nicer than the patter of little feet around the house again, especially when you know that your kids are soon going to be taking their kids home to give grandma and grandad a quiet evening on their own!

In many ways, grandparents seem to get on with their grandchildren better than parents do, maybe because parents are too busy raising children to enjoy them as much as grandparents can. The great knack of dealing with a seven year old, we have found, is to be able to behave like a seven year old yourself – and it's a skill that seems to have grown on us as we have both got older.

The quickest way for any grandparent to get a grandchild's full attention is to sit down and look as though you're just about to take a nap. But we're very glad that our grandchildren, Gemma, Victoria, James, Louise, Thomas, Hannah and Samuel, live close enough to visit us regularly, and we hope they get as much out of these frequent meetings as we do.

It's always sad when grandparents and grandchildren don't get to meet each other very often – whether it's through distance, or indifference. The two generations have a lot to offer each other, and, as this book shows, buckets of love flow across the age gap when a caring family keeps in touch regularly. Grandchildren are a great confirmation of life, a source of joy and energy for older people. For children, interested grandparents are an unfailing source of alleged wisdom, old jokes, tall tales, dodgy advice, too many sweets, and good old fashioned cuddles. (And the bonus is they can always spill the beans on how badly behaved your parents were as children.)

Enjoy the book. If you haven't been in touch with your grandparents or grandchildren lately, pick up the phone. But don't do it together, you'll both get the engaged signal.

Jimmy and Irene Greaves
Little Baddow, Essex

*From left to right:* Nanadot (great-gran), Nanpam, Granjack, Dusty, the dog, and Granjack's loganberry bush in the garden.

**Jamie Goddard,** aged 4

**Jamie Goddard,** aged 4

**Philippa Hilton,** aged 7

MY GRaNDMa
and
GRaNDaD
I like my GRaNDMa
and GRaNDaD
because they give me
Strawberry's
from their garden,
and my GRaNDMa
gives me Strawberry
jam every Saturday.

I Like
my GRaNDMa
and
GRaNDaD

My grandad likes gardening
My gran likes knitting and
Baking cakes

**Becky Maynard**

**Lisa Gamble,** aged 7

My Gramma loves me very much
she thinks the world of me. she gives us
lots of money to spend on sweets
and things we like. and takes us
on holidays bye the sea.
my Gramma loves me. and I love
her to.

**Peggy Seymour,** aged 7

**Shane Rollins,** aged 6

I know a grampa whos
The best in the whole wide
world. Do you?

Do you know a grampa whos the
Best in the whole wide world?
I do & its my grampa!
Hes the best in the whole wide world.
Hes very nice to me he lets me
draw on his paper.
He gives me biscits and sweets
to eat they all taste very good
But theres only one thing I can tell
you about my grampa that is thats,
that hes the best grampa in the
WHOLE WIDE WORLD!

**Anon,**
*from St Neots,
Cambridgeshire*

my granny lives in a flat
and she goes to chapel
and she spoils me I love
her and she love me
and I think shes pretty

**Rhian Parker,** aged 6

Grandmas and Grandads
Grandma and Grandad are so
Kind to me,
They Sometimes let me sit
on their knee.
They both play games to
make me glad,
They're the best Grandma and
Grandad I've ever had.
They let me sleep when mum
goes out,
Or stay in the garden and
2. play about.
; We watch t.v. and snuggle
up,
With in one hand a mug
or cup.
They both love me lots and
lots,
Especially when I wash the
pots.
I love them too with all
my heart,
And I hope we'll never be
taken apart.

Katie Craven

My Grandad's a superman
I call him Grandad Hook
For when he lost his arm, it was his best one they took.
But with his left one he writes now, just as good as before,
And he pretends to nip me with his hook as I run out the door.
He's not so good at snooker as he can't quite grip the cue
But he's an ace at crosswords even though he's 82!

Michael Simpson, aged 8

My Gran

Ben

I love my Gran because she makes up funny jokes.

Ben Mostyn, aged 5

This is my nan sitting in her deck chair in her Garden

Claire, aged 7

My Granny is a very good cook and she knits lovely jumpers

Chloe Cairns age 10

**Chloë Cairns,** aged 10

**Sarah Mason,** aged 10½

I have two Grandmothers but both Grandfathers died before I was born. I feel very lucky to have such nice Grandmothers, especially Grandma Hayward who is quite old but has come to live with us. I have a lovely Mummy and Daddy who both have very demanding jobs and although my Mummy is very generous in buying me sweets and novelties she is always so busy that I am sure the reason why I love my Grandmas so much is because they give me <u>Time</u>, especially the one who lives with me. <u>Time</u> to meet me from school and listen to my good and bad days. <u>Time</u> to teach me to make buns and cakes, sewing and knitting. <u>Time</u> to tell or read bed-time stories. I feel that other persons' time is the best present to have especially from my dear Grandma and that is why I love her so much.

**Anne-Marie Hall,** aged 10

Dear Sir I am talking a bowt my nan she is owase give me Jewelry and she is owase good to me and she owase byes me feed and me to pick strawberrys and take me to T.J.Shop Love Linsey age 6 xx

**Lynsey O'Connell,** aged 6

I like my Grandad because he is nice. and he is squashy because he is fat. and cuddly too. on Thursday I am going on the train to my nans and Grandad's in Hereford.

Bonnita Franklin, aged 7

I like my Grandpresents becduse they Give me thigs and They knit me cardigars. I help pop in The garden and I sometimes go To The shops for her. They are the best grandparents. I love Them very Moch.

Robert Hoodley, aged 8

**Jamie Harriman,** aged 10½

I love my gran because she spoils me silly.

**Emily Gray,** aged 11

# Grandparents

My Granny is always messing about.
She's always got the kettle on!
She's always rushing to the shops.
My granny has got blonde hair.
She wears an apron.
She is absolutely mad on crosswords.
She always wears one of them funny nets
on her head that has got weird patterns
on them.
My Gran is 59, but she doesn't look it.
My grandad always sits in an old rocking
chair with his glasses and slippers on.
He smells of tobacco because he smokes
a pipe.
And He is always telling me stories
and taking me places.
My other grandad is similar but he wears
iluminous shirts and he's always in his
sunhouse or in the garden, even if it is
raining!

By Jamie Harriman

**Jamie Harriman,** aged 10½

Nan and Auntie Janet

**Simon Curran,** aged 7

I love my Grandma and Grandad the best because if Mum or Dad says 'no', I always ask Grandma Mavis or Grandad David and they say 'yes'.

**Gemma Hicks,** aged 4

**Melissa Proverbs,** aged 10¾

## Grandparent

I think that my nan is not soft or strict and I'm not just saying this because shes my nan she buys us presents but she doesn't spoil us. She is also very clever and does alot of crosswords.

**Lucy Williamson,** aged 8

My Nanna, Doris, who has a dog called Toffee
**Alison Dunlop,** aged 6

## My Grandparents

I am lucky,
Luckier than most.
Most people have
Two or four
Grandparents
But I have six.

Six kisses
Six hugs
Six smiling faces
Six grandparents
All in a row.
I am lucky,
Luckier than most.

**Diane Matthews,** aged 7¾

Grandad Jack

my Grandad Jack
Went to Heven th June

I loved my Grandad
Jack Very much

and it was sad

he played tunes on
his mouth organ

he chased me and my

brother with his

walking stick and we

used to hide it

Grandads mouth organ

he sang me some songs

I shall always love my

Grandad Jack

and gave us sweets.

Sweets

Christopher Ardley, aged 6

my grandma gives me money she is kind and I love her her hair is yellow

**Stacey Jones,** aged 6

## My Grandparents

My grandparents are great. I stay at weekends. My Grandad is 62 and he has had an open heart operation. My little cousin is 2½ and he lives with Nan and Grandad. Grandad takes us walks with the dogs we collect the eggs from the hens we pick redcurrants and broad beans with him he has a lot of patience with us we go to dog and hen shows with him too. Grandad had to have glasses and he let me go with him to pick the frames and he had the ones I liked. Nanny is 52. She is very under standing more than my mum we bake together she reads to me and she lets my friends sleep in the school holidays. Nanny takes my cousin and me on the bus with Grandad's tokens, Grandad takes Rhys and me on his motor bike round the grass. My Grandad built us a sandpit and bought us a guinea pig each. I love my grandparents because they care about us and nothing is to much trouble for them, and they dont get angry.

**Emma Cannon,** aged 10

My gran died last week and it just isn't the same without her. She's always been a real lady, she would put lipstick on and spray herself with perfume even in her eighties. She had a stroke. She wouldn't eat, she looked so feeble. I gave her a drink and held her hand. She was blind. I would tell her I loved her, I wanted to make sure she knew that. After many days of suffering she died peacefully in her sleep. I saw her a few days later in her coffin. She still looked a real lady, my gran.

**Imogen Bunch,** aged 9

My Nan Likes to go to the garden

Anon, *from Nettlebed, Oxfordshire*

I love nanny and
Grandad because they are
funny, happy, and special
people.

Helene Rachael Jones, aged 4

**Ben Smith,** aged 9¾

**Andrew Mee,** aged 9¾

my daddy's mummy

my mummy's daddy

Olivia Garbutt, aged 8

## Grandparents

My grandma has got grey hair and glasses. She is a little old fashioned. She is very kind and is always giving Me sweets and she gives me a lot of Money on my birthday and christmas she wears a checked pina and slippers She takes care of My uncle doing his dinner because he is not married. She goes up town on saturday with her friends.

## My grandad isn't alive now.

He wasn't very healthy because he kept smoking and going to the pub. He was 70 and had got a walking stick and he gave me sweets. lived for about a month and died of pneumonia.

by

Paul Meer.

**Paul Meer,** aged 10¹/₂

this is my Grandpa he loves gardening

Katy Scottorn, aged 8

I LOVE
MY Grandma and Grandpa
bECaUSE  thEY LOVE mE
and mY SiSter.

**Rebecca Epps,** aged 5½

# My Granny.

I love my Granny.
My Granny buys us sweets.
We stay with her at Christmas,
And she gets us lots of treats.

My Granny doesnt drive a car,
She goes on a bus,
Or a train,
When its far.

My Granny has a pet.
He is a dog called Charlie,
She also had another dog,
My brothers never met.

My Granny has lots of friends,
And relatives, too.
We all love her,
Yes we do, oh, yes we do.

My Granny has short curly hair,
Her eyes are sort of green,
And, to me, she is far more,
Important than the queen.

**Shane Warde**

**Louise McCann,** aged 10

My granny is the best
granny because she
makes lovey cakes and
pancakes

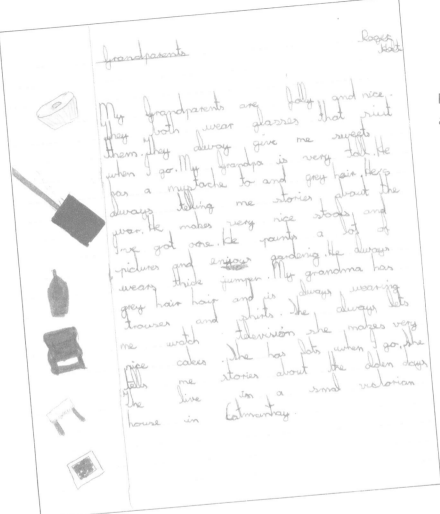

**Roger Holt,** aged 10

Nothing is too much trouble for my Nannie. When we are bord and fed up she makes us a tent with a clothes airer and an old sheet, and dresses us up with her old clothes. She makes us pastry with four and water and lets us play rolling it out and cutting up shapes. If it is too much trouble for Mommy it's never too much trouble for Nannie.

**Joanne Phipps,** aged 8

**Donna Reeve,** aged 10¾

# Grandparents

My grandparents are a funny old couple. Whenever I am at their house it's always gambling! My mamma doesn't look old fashioned. She's trendy and she likes pop music. My grandad on the other hand is very particular at dinner time. He asks for twelve chips, no more, no less! He has a bald head on top and grey at each side. My mamma's hair is ginger and she is absoluty crazy.

By - Donna Reeve

**Clare Hill,** aged 10¼

evre mone my nanny tack Her
dog fra walking and He is called
oly.

**Carolina Loveridge,** aged 8

My grandpa wears bermuda shorts and he takes me over all otments I love the him because he tells jokes

**Kelly Evans,** aged 6

Owen Dobson

My Granny &
Grandad are very
Kind. They give
me pockcet
money and they
give me lots
of cuddles.
My granny makes
me lots of
things for
tea.

**Owen Dobson,** aged 6

my grampy works in
a toyshop
I love nimond hesells
toys

**Andrew Foxon,** aged 7

I think my granny is funny because she always says things like 'If you see two nests at the top of a tree in Spring, you will have a hot summer!'

I love my granny because when ever she comes she showers us with presents

When ever my granny comes I have a sudden urge to knit and sew because she always manages to knit a jumper when ever she comes.

There once was a granny from Troon
Who lived in a gas-filled balloon.
The higher she flew
The less people knew
Of the songs that she sang, out of tune.

**Emily Mostyn,** aged 11

They babysit for us
all the time for
free

if we fall grandma
is the best one to
help because she is
a very important
person in the st John's
Ambulance

lets us stay for tea
While my mom goes
to aerobic's,

She always has good
ideas to do when we
are bored

Makes lovely bilberry
Dumplings on special
Sundays when its
Someone's Birthday or
annivesary

Makes us laugh
when he teases
my Great Grandma

Tricks us at birthdays
when he wraps a small
present and when he
puts it in a really big
box so we get exited

He is very dumsy like
a clown

He tries to do
Lizzie's Work out
tape with Grandma
(I bet he looks funny)

Sola and Simon Bramley,
aged 8 and 9

This is my Grandad he is walking a Dog

**Steven,** aged 8

MY Gran

**Tracey Comibert,** aged 11

Kathleen Davies, aged 6

I LIKE MY GRANDAD
BECAUSE he loves me

my Grandparents

My Grandma and Grandad are special
because they always help me and
they are always there When I need
them and they always try to get
to all my football matches even
When it is cold and it rains.
They do too many things for me
and my sister and our cousins that
I can't write it all down.
I just Love them both very much.

Phillip Hubbard, aged 7½

I like my Gramy because she has a lovely grden by Jacob

ayn 7

**Jacob,** aged 7

I love my Nan because even though she has lots of grandchildren she still has time for me. She plays lots of games with me and tells me stories of the old days. We sing lots of songs together. Even though she's my only Nan I wouldn't want any more, because I love her so much and I know she loves me.

**Lindsay Atherton,** aged 8

My grandmother likes watching T.V.

Clare Hill

I love my CRandparents
becouse they let me go on
the swing and I hove lots
of fun
on the swing

**Jonathan Flooit,** aged 5

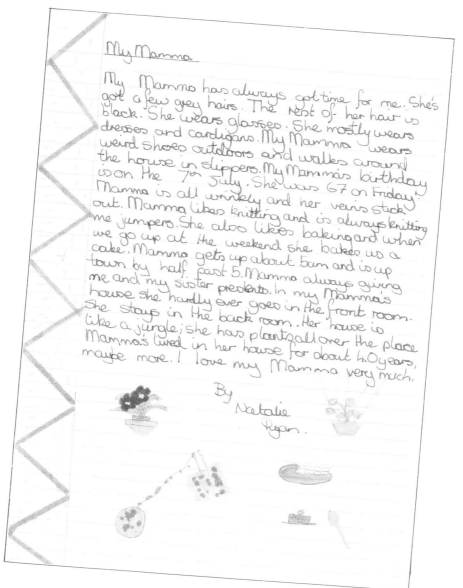

## My Mamma

My Mamma has always got time for me. She's got a few grey hairs. The rest of her hair is black. She wears glasses. She mostly wears dresses and cardigans. My Mamma wears weird shoes outdoors and walks around the house in slippers. My Mamma's birthday is on the 7th July. She was 67 on Friday. Mamma is all wrinkly and her veins stick out. Mamma likes knitting and is always knitting me jumpers. She also likes baking and when we go up at the weekend she bakes us a cake. Mamma gets up about 5am and is up town by half past 5. Mamma always giving me and my sister presents. In my Mamma's house she hardly ever goes in the front room. She stays in the back room. Her house is like a jungle; she has plants all over the place. Mamma's lived in her house for about 40 years, maybe more. I love my Mamma very much.

By Natalie Ryan.

Natalie Ryan, aged 10

WHY i LIKE MY GRAND PARENTS

WHY I LIKE MY GRANDPARENTS.

i like my grandparents
because they buy me lots
of toys in my bedroom
we got about 100 toys.
every time i go down my
nans i always have some
toys waiting for me.
Love FROM KELLY FOX.

Coloring book

**Kelly Fox**

grandpa    grandma

**Anon,**
*from Pinner, Middlesex*

I love my Nana Close because when Mommy and Daddy have to go out Nana babysits and she is always there when we need her and she brings me sweets evrey Wednesday and Sunday and she is kind and I love my Nana because she gives me my favourite mins pie evrey Sunday and when I don't want something I say I don't want that, Nana, and she does not give me it. One day I gave my Nana 2 pounds and she went to the town and she got me a yo-yo and that is why I love my Nana.

## Nana Close coming to our house
**Paul Rogan,** aged 7

O.A.P.

My Gran's just had her birthday,
She was seventy-three,
And she has pulled in a form,
That makes her an O.A.P.!!

The form

G randma
R ainy days for grandmas
A ren't
N ice.
D ull days for grandads are weak.
P roper days for grandma
A nd grandad are
R adiant. The
E nd of
N ight
T ings and the
S un shines bright.

**Anna Crossland,** aged 7

**Nicky Crossland,** aged 9½

This is Granny and pappy my pappy is older than my Granny. She is as old as a Dinosaur. I love Dinosaurs very moch. I love pappy because he grows me lovely parsnips and Strawberries onhis allotment

**Lauren Pavli,** aged 5

## Grandmas

**G**reat for fun
**R**eally kind
**A**lways generous and treating us
**N**ever nasty
**D**oting on us
**M**aking us sweaters
**A**lways loving
**S**o special is Grandma

**Joanne Tarry,** aged 12

I LOVE my nan and pap because they always have lots of food for us

**Cheryl Allsopp,** aged 9

# MY Grandads Slippers

My grandad Wears Slippers
He buys them From the shop.
He's got over A hundred pairs
My nana Says Stop□ Stop□.

Stop this lark stop buying Slipers
We cann't Afond A pair oF knikers
yes My DeAr I promise I'll Stop
I'll take them back To the shop.

**Abigail Stockley,** aged 9

**Richard Smith,** aged 10

# Grandparents

My grandparents are an old little pair. My grandad takes me fishing on a boat. He is very well built with grey hair and a bald patch in the middle. He has broad shoulders and he is about 6 foot 7. He takes me diving and swimming. My grandma buys me things that my mum won't buy and I don't get shouted at. I get lots of sweets and biscuits and I have to eat cauliflower and mushy peas. They are things that I don't like. but my grandparents. mean well.

**Rose Cairns,** aged 9

My Gran can cycle faster than any granny in our street.
My granny can bake the most scrumptious cakes and
she is always cleaning. She can knit dead neat jumpers
and cardigans and can do the most groovy dances I've
ever seen. When she does her exercises with her Jane
Fonda tape she can do them much faster than me and
never has to stop.

**Nicola Deeney**

Mummy's parents
I like my mum's parents playing golf.

**Matthew McHugo,** aged 9

Daddy's Mummy
I like her apple cramble.

by Matthew McHugo aged 9

**Samantha Boyle,** aged 10

This is Elsie Johnstone she is my mums mum.

**Jessica Barry,** aged 11

## Grandad

(1) My Grandad is a very determand man,
I can't do as many things he can.
He's always hard at work,
He never will stop,
Unless I offer him some Whiskey and some pop.

(2) He's a very brave man,
He fought in the Vietnam.
He got medals for his chest.
He was always the best,
And (1)He still is now.

**Lily Winder,** aged 6

I LOVE my Grand-
Parents very much because
they feed me more than my mum
does. and plays more games wiht me.
from Sarah BartleTT xxx♡♡♡x
x x x x x

**Sarah Bartlett,** aged 7

I Love My Nanna and Grandad because they are nice and happy. Some times they give us Sweets. I Love them because they Love us. I Love my Nanna and Grandad because thay have time to Spend with us and do Special things with me and My two sisters

Catherine Ann Jones, aged 6

Dear TU-AM,

I love my grandparents because they are so kind and nice to me. They always buy me lots of nice presents and cards for my birthday and christmas. When I was little my gramma used to always take me home from school because my dad was at work. If I am ever ill at school they always come and collect me from school and then I stay with them for the rest of the day. (I am not ill very often.)

**Jenny Stiles,** aged 11

## My grandma

My grandma is kind,
She's got a loving mind.
She gives me sweets,
And lots more treats.
My grandma is a dear,
She brings me good cheer.
On her you can depend,
She gives me money to spend.
If something makes me cry,
Upon grandma I can always rely.
For sympathy and lots of tenderness,
Grandma is definably the best.

**Alison Mercer,** aged 10

MY NAN IN CARTON FORM.

My Grandad in carton form

Jamie Reeve, aged 12

I love Nanny because she has lots of goodies in her fridge - not like our fridge.

I love Grandad because he worked so hard in the garden building that great big wall, just for me to sit on.

Aaron Woods, aged 3

**Mark Watkins,** aged 7

I help my grandcha
in the garden. He
tells me funny jokes
and I love him

**Thomas Lewis,** aged 6

I love my grancha
he works as a
Shop keepe and he
has got budgies

**Russell Parker,** aged 6

my granny works
the allotments who up
grows vegetables he

I love my grandma
because she gives
me some sweets she
has got a kind
face

**Anne-Marie Jones,** aged 6

## My Grandad

I'm my Grandads best Pal
He plays with me
My Grandads got brown eyes
and a fat tummy
He says "Hello my best Mate"
and buys me sweets at Sainsburys.

Jonathan Anslow, aged 6

I love my grandad
and he always
teases me all the
time

Jonathan McDonough, aged 7

Jonathan Anslow, aged 6

**Ian Lambert,** aged 10

## My Grandad

He      comes    to   tea
      with     mum   and   dad   he
Some times      shows   us  how to add.
He     tells   us  off  when   we   are   bad
but   cheers   me   up  when    I    am  sad.

Karen Guy, aged 11

I think my nanny and grandad are good because they look after me and my sister sometimes for the night. And I think it was two weeks ago when they invited my family for a barbeque. It was there own one We had some chickin legs and pork chops And last we had some corn on the cob, toasted rolls and some salud. They used to live in London. And I did not like that because we could only stay for a weekend now and again. But now they live in Northampton and i can see them a lot more. My nanny makes cakes, She calls them bounty cakes because they have chocolate chips and coconut in. They taste quite nice. My grandad goes riding His horse is called charlie. He looks after charlie and usually goes on Saturday. They like it now because they are retired and can do all the things they want to do. I think my nanny and grandad are the best I could have.

Paul Howe, aged 9

**Jessica Brunt,** aged 10

I Love my Granny. beacause She takes
me out and she buys sweetsI
Love my Grandpa beacause he
brings sweets back from work.
They both play with me and they love
me.

I Love my

Grandparents !

**Hannah Burrows,** aged 7

Grandma

Hayley Culverwell, aged 9

My Granny and Grandpa love me. My Granny has hurt
her foot, she has crutches. She likes to sit in the sun.
She gives us biscits and my Grandpar likes gardening.

**Amy,** aged 7

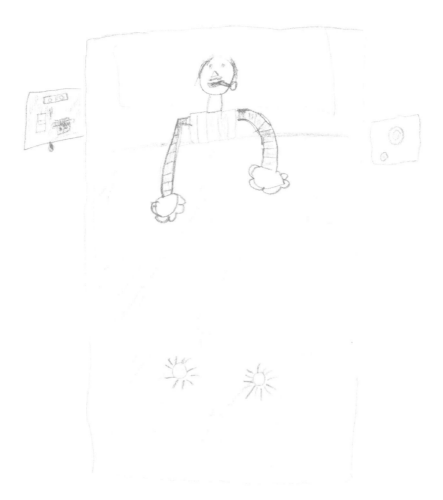

This is when popper
was in bed be cose he
had cancer and I looked after him

Tom, aged 7

my Grandad } my nan
He eat pepmints } she a can
He so proud } She makes Jam
Hes my Grandad } she's my nan.

Trudy Cone, aged 12

My poem for nanny

Nannys are loved alot
but you are the best
by us sweets
never get a rest
You get us treats as you walk around the streets
O nanny I love you lots and lots
O nanny I love you lots.

Clare Fogarty, aged 6

my Gran is a Super Gran
Because she is good to me and she
Looks after me I Love her and she
makes me Lots of cakes She lets
me eat her cherries and
Currents out of the Pantry
She lets me make Cakes
She washes me She plays with
me she lets me drink sherry
She takes me to the toileT
She takes me to the Park
She Looks after me and my
Brother when my Mom and Dap
are out She looks after my
GranDap She listens to my Jokes
and laughs my Gran is the
Best Gran in the world and
She Loves me

From Gareth Rees age 6

Gareth Rees, aged 6

**Suzie Allsopp,** aged 5

i love my
nan and pap
becavse ther
are fvll of
cvadies

well   I   love   my   grandpa   and   grandma
because   they   buy   me   and   my   sister
lot's   of   Sweets   and   they   are   very   very
kind   they   take   us   out   and   they   dont
Smack   us   or   tell   us   off   and   they
love   me   alot   as   well   as   my
Sister

Lisa Vaisey, aged 9

**Samantha Roney,** aged 9

Grandad Dixson

Dear TV-AM,

I'am writing to you about my Grandad Charles who is the nicest Grandad anybody could ever have. My grand-ma died last year and since then my grandad always looks after me during School holidays but he looks after my Sister every-day because my mum and dad have to go to work. He always takes us out and we always have a good time. He is always laughing and we love him very much.

**Louise Foad,** aged 9

I love my Gran. She is 70 years old but she wants to be 21. She has just had a new perm.

**Lucy Wilks**

**My Nanna and Grandad**

It is with sadness that I no longer have a Grandad. He was called to rest suddenly two years ago. He was a lovely person who loved us all especially my Nanna. My Nanna is a very special lady, apart from losing her husband, two of her sons have also been killed. She loves everyone she meets, is kind, considerate, and has a very lovely nature. We share many happy hours together and have great fun, and she is my best friend. Nannas are a very important part of one's life - especially if you have one like mine.

**Clare Dulson,** aged 10¾

Grann and Gandad go fo a Wak

They walk past the houses looking at the sea.
Grandad wonders how much that house would be.
Granny wonders what to make for tea before
Emmerdale farm comes on TV.

**Mahala Dawson,** aged 7

## Grandparents

My grandad is a nice Man. He tells me about birds and parrots. He wears warm comfy slippers. He wears a big Jacket and warm body Jumpers underneath. his socks are luminous green and they Are warm and cozy inside. He has got a lot of birds. He doesn't go out alot. He has a flat cap. He has got some bird video He lets Me watch them He wears glasses He is a nice man.

My Grandmare has a woofly warm Jumper. My granmare goes out a few times. I like both grandparents.

Adam Gutteridge,
aged 10

Here are two poems about my grandma and Grandad. (They are both 24 words)

1. Grandads radios
   My Grandad collects radios
   Which gets right up my grandmas nose,
   She says they take up too much space
   And gather dust in any case.

2. My Grandad

   He has two little green houses
   That me and my sister play in
   We stand on all the cabbages
   And never have to pay him.

**Hannah Dawson,** aged 10

I like my nanny

I like my nanny BECAUSE she is always funny and she is mine.

Jade Franklin, aged 5

grandma in her overall

I love my grandma because she gives me
lots of sweets and she makes me lots of
clothes and she looks after my vegetable
and flower garden when I go home and
she gives me presents and lots of cuddles
and she loves me

Mervin Downs, aged 6

# My Grandad          Davina

My Grandad is a sunny
kind of person. He wobbles
and shakes from side to
side. He is a very fat
person. He wears thick woolly
jumpers and has frilly
khickers. He gives me pocket
money. I love my Grandad.
He loves to play scrabble.

**Davina Atchison,** aged 10¼

MY FRANDMA

I LOVE MY FRANDMA BECAUSE
SHE SOMETIMES COMES TO SEE ME
AND PLAYS NICE GAMES WITH ME
SHE EVEN BRINGS ME HALIFAX COMICS.

Victoria Moone, aged 4

my nana and grandad are the
best in the world becouse my
nana bakes buns for me and my
grandad plays with me. I like sleeping at
their house because I sneak into
their bed and put my cold toes
on grandads tummy and nana reads me
stories.

Victoria Roberts, aged 6

I help my grampy
up the garden and
I helped him make
a new shed I love him
because he lets me pick
the potatoes and peel
them

**Craig Jolliffe,** aged 6